Stocking Stumpers

Chicago Bears

By S. Claus

RED-LETTER PRESS, INC.
Saddle River, New Jersey

Red-Letter Press, Inc.
P.O. Box 393, Saddle River, NJ 07458
www.Red-LetterPress.com
info@Red-LetterPress.com

ACKNOWLEDGMENTS
SANTA'S SUBORDINATE CLAUSES

Compiled By:
Jeff Kreismer

Editor:
Jack Kreismer

Cover Design:
Cliff Behum

Special Mention:
Lyn Thomas

" Nobody who ever gave his best regretted it."

-Papa Bear, George Halas

INTRODUCTION

Whether you're having a few quiet
moments to yourself or enjoying a
reunion with friends and family, Stocking
Stumpers is the perfect holiday companion.
Gather 'round the Christmas tree or simply
kick back in your easy chair while
trying out the holiday humdingers,
tailor-made tests and trivia tidbits.

Once you've had a sampling, I think you'll
agree, Stocking Stumpers is proof of the
Christmas pudding that good things do
come in small packages. Ho ho ho!

Merry Christmas!!

S. Claus

The Mantle Meter

'Tis right around Christmas
and all through the book,

There are all sorts of stumpers
everywhere that you look.

There are quizzes and seasonal tests
to take you to task,

But what are those "stocking"
questions you ask?

Well, the stockings are hung
by the chimney with care.

The more that are filled,
the tougher the bear.

And so it is that
the Mantle Meter keeps score,

Rating the stumpers,
one stocking or more.

STOCKING STUMPERS

CHICAGO BEARS

FIRST AND FIVE

1. In 2012, what two Bears became the first teammates in NFL history to each return an interception for a touchdown in consecutive games?

2. The first player ever drafted by the Chicago Bears, way back in 1936, wound up in the Pro Football Hall of Fame. Do you know him?

3. In 2001, who became the first Bear to catch 100 passes in a single season?

4. Who was the first head coach to lead the Bears to more than 13 wins in a season?

5. The Bears played in their first-ever postseason overtime game in 2007 when they defeated what team?

In 1934, what Bear became the first player in NFL history to rush for 1,000 yards in one season?

ANSWERS

1.

Charles Tillman and Lance Briggs

2.

Joe Stydahar

3.

Marty Booker

4.

Mike Ditka, in 1985

5.

Seattle Seahawks, 27-24

Beattie Feathers

HISTORY 101

1. When the Chicago Bears began play in 1920, the franchise operated under what name?

2. When the Bears signed this Hall of Famer days after his final college game, it led the NFL to implement a rule saying a player couldn't be signed until his college's senior class graduated.

3. Between 1933-63, the Bears played in ten NFL Championship games. What team did they meet six times in those contests, going 4-2?

4. Including the answer to #2, in 1963, three Bears were honored in the first year of inductions into the new Pro Football Hall of Fame. Who were they?

5. Who was the only man to be a part of both the Bears 1963 and 1985 championships?

Who split the kick return duties with Devin Hester in 2008 and wound up leading the league with a 29.7 average?

ANSWERS

1.

Decatur Staleys

2.

Red Grange

3.

New York Giants

4.

George Halas, Bronko
Nagurski and Red Grange

5.

Mike Ditka, as a player and coach

Danieal Manning

FUMBLEROOSKI

1. What Bear's first career touchdown came in the 1985 NFC Championship Game vs. the Rams on a 52-yard fumble return?

2. In Super Bowl XX, the Bears would surrender three quick points to New England after what runner fumbled on just the second play of the game?

3. What Chicago defensive back's four forced fumbles in a single game was the most ever by one player since the NFL started tracking the stat?

4. In 1923, George Halas set a record that stood for decades by stripping a player of the ball and returning the fumble 98 yards for a score. What sports legend did he victimize?

5. What Bear became a goat in a 2011 loss at Denver after going out of bounds rather than running time late in the fourth quarter and fumbling away the game in overtime?

This 1950s Bear is the only man to throw a touchdown pass to both Mike Ditka and John Mackey, the first two tight ends to become Hall of Famers.

ANSWERS

1.

Wilber Marshall

2.

Walter Payton

3.

Charles Tillman, in 2012 vs. the Titans

4.

Jim Thorpe

5.

Marion Barber

Ed Brown

THE KANSAS COMET

1. Gale Sayers opted to sign with the Bears after what AFL team also drafted him in 1965?

2. Sayers set the NFL record for the most single-season touchdowns by a rookie, with 22. He also tied a record by scoring how many TDs in one game?

3. After coming back from knee surgery, Sayers received the Halas Courage Award in 1970. However, instead of accepting it for himself, he passed it on to what teammate?

4. Fact or Fib? Because his career was so brief, Sayers was the youngest person ever inducted into the Pro Football Hall of Fame.

5. In which category is Gale Sayers the NFL's all-time leader?
   a. Yards per carry   b. Kick return average
   c. Yards per reception

❄ SEASONAL STUMPER ❄

On December 26, 1982, the Bears beat the Rams despite making some rare NFL history. They had never before allowed a 400-yard passer, but let what quarterback, whose first name mirrors that of a *Four Christmases* star, throw for 509 yards and 3 TDs?

ANSWERS

1.

Kansas City Chiefs

2.

Six

3.

Brian Piccolo

4.

Fact, at age 34

5.

b

Seasonal Stumper Answer:

Vince Ferragamo, of the L.A. Rams
(Vince Vaughn is the actor of the 2008 comedy.)

DYNAMIC DUOS

1. What two Bears finished first and second in the 2000 NFL Defensive Rookie of the Year voting?

2. The first time the Bears had two 1,000-yard receivers in the same season occurred in 1995. Who were they?

3. Jay Cutler formed a solid QB-WR combo with this player at Vanderbilt before they again joined forces in Chicago in 2009.

4. What two Bears were named the Defensive Player of the Month in back-to-back months in 2012?

5. In the first round of the 1965 NFL Draft, the Bears wound up selecting what two Hall of Famers?

What coach led the Bears to their worst season in franchise history in 1969 when they went 1-13?

ANSWERS

1.

Brian Urlacher and Mike Brown, respectively

2.

Jeff Graham and Curtis Conway

3.

Earl Bennett

4.

Tim Jennings and Charles Tillman

5.

Dick Butkus and Gale Sayers

Jim Dooley

THE SUPER BOWL SHUFFLE

1. The idea for the Bears *Super Bowl Shuffle* rap song was born when what leading receiver approached teammates about the idea of cutting a video to raise money for charity?

2. Ironically, the Bears shot the video the day after their only loss of the 1985 season. Who took them down?

3. What eventual Super Bowl champs put out their own record in 1984, the year before the *Super Bowl Shuffle*?

4. What Bears Hall of Famer declined participation in the song because he was afraid it was too arrogant?

5. Fact or Fib? *Super Bowl Shuffle* won a Grammy for best R&B song by a group.

What two linebackers on the 1985 Super Bowl champion Bears later became head coaches in the NFL?

ANSWERS

1.

   Willie Gault

2.

   Miami Dolphins, 38-24

3.

   San Francisco 49ers *(We Are the 49ers)*

4.

   Dan Hampton

5.

   Fib – It was nominated, however.

Ron Rivera and Mike Singletary

A LEAGUE OF THEIR OWN

1. What 1970s Bears safety was named the head coach of the Arena Football League's Orlando Predators in 2012?

2. Before he and his brother, Darren, both became Canadian Football League stars, he won the only game he started as a Bear in 1986. Who is he?

3. What founding owner of the Arena League's Chicago Bruisers in 1987 was the last active Bears player to have played for George Halas?

4. What one-time Bears head coach is the only man to ever coach teams in the NFL, college football, the USFL, World Football League and CFL?

5. What Bears Pro Bowl returner was later a GM of the Arena League's Austin Wranglers?

What Bear led the NFL in interceptions in 2012?

ANSWERS

1.

Doug Plank

2.

Doug Flutie

3.

Doug Buffone, who retired in 1980

4.

Jack Pardee

5.

Glyn Milburn

Tim Jennings, with 9

SHOW BUSINESS BEARS

1.
Who starred as Brian Piccolo in the 1971 ABC network movie *Brian's Song*?

2.
What player portrayed himself in Brian's Song and was later a regular character on TV shows such as *My Two Dads* and *Hang Time*.

3.
What Bear was the first football player ever to appear on a box of Wheaties?

4.
What does "Bill Swerski's Superfans" have to do with the Bears?

5.
What Bears legend starred alongside Will Ferrell in the 2005 comedy film, *Kicking and Screaming*?

❄ SEASONAL STUMPER ❄

Born in Santa Claus, Indiana, what "giving" quarterback was the last Bear to lead the league in passes intercepted?

ANSWERS

1.

James Caan

2.

Dick Butkus

3.

Red Grange

4. It was the name of the recurring sketch about Chicago sports fans, especially "Da Bears" on *Saturday Night Live*.

5.

Mike Ditka

Seasonal Stumper Answer:

Jay Cutler, with 26 in 2009

FIRST TIME'S A CHARM
SUPER BOWL XX

1. The Bears entered Super Bowl XX vs. the Patriots having shut out their previous two postseason opponents. Who were they?

2. In their 46-10 rout of New England, what Patriot became the only player to reach the end zone in the 1985 Playoffs against Chicago?

3. Which Bear did *not* score a touchdown in the game?
   a. William Perry   b. Dan Hampton
   c. Matt Suhey   d. Reggie Phillips

4. The Bears set single-game Super Bowl records for the most sacks and the fewest rushing yards allowed. Ironically, it was the same number. What?

5. Who was named the game's MVP with 1.5 sacks and two forced fumbles?

What NFL division do the Bears play in?

ANSWERS

1.
Giants (21-0) and Rams (24-0)

2.
Irving Fryar, on a TD pass
from Steve Grogan

3.
b

4.
7

5.
Richard Dent

NFC North

PASSING FADS

1. From 2002-2007, the Bears had a different passing leader each year. How many of the six QBs can you name?

2. What Bears signal-caller set a then-NFL record by throwing for 468 yards and six touchdowns in a 1949 game?

3. What 1990s quarterback was the first ever to have multiple 3,000-yard passing seasons in Chicago?

4. Beginning in 1986, who won his first ten career starts in the NFL as Chicago's quarterback?

5. Jim McMahon finished his NFL career with two Super Bowl rings- one with Chicago and one as a backup with what squad?

"They are who we thought they were." Who said it?

ANSWERS

1.

Jim Miller, Kordell Stewart, Chad Hutchinson, Kyle Orton, Rex Grossman and Brian Griese

2.

Johnny Lujack

3.

Erik Kramer

4.

Mike Tomczak

5.

Green Bay Packers (Super Bowl XXXI)

Denny Green, in a post-game tirade after his Cardinals blew a 20-point lead over the Bears in 2006

DA BEARS

Each of these answers begins with "Da".

1. He and Mike Ditka both went to the University of Pittsburgh and coached the Bears.

2. Bears Hall of Famer Ed Healey, called the "most versatile tackle ever" by George Halas, went to this Ivy League school.

3. While they gave up a TD pass to former Bear Kyle Orton, Chicago beat this team, 34-18, in 2012 before 90,080 fans in the NFL's biggest stadium.

4. This offensive lineman, who later became a tight ends coach for the Saints, was the only man to play for and coach under Mike Ditka.

5. Jay Cutler's then-fiancée Kristin Cavallari was a contestant on this television show in 2011.

What defensive tackle caught Erik Kramer's lone postseason touchdown pass as a Bear in a 1995 loss to the 49ers?

ANSWERS

1.

Dave Wannstedt

2.

Dartmouth

3.

Dallas (Cowboys Stadium)

4.

Dan Neal

5.

Dancing with the Stars

Jim Flanigan

There's a Draft in Here

1. When was the last time the Bears chose a quarterback with a top-five pick?

2. In 1958 and '60, the Bears drafted a future Super Bowl MVP and a Pro Bowl quarterback, both who had their success in Dallas. Can you name either?

3. What Heisman Trophy winner did the Bears select in the 1995 NFL Draft?

4. The Bears shipped Mike Ditka to Philly in 1967 for a player who was the #1 overall pick in the 1964 AFL Draft. Who?

5. What 1983 eighth-round Bears draft pick would become a Pro Bowler who played in double-digit postseason games with Chicago?

❄ Seasonal stumpeR ❄

He was born January 1, 1944 and shares his first name with the former *New Year's Rockin' Eve* host.
In 1965, his first career NFL score came on the only touchdown pass ever thrown by Gale Sayers. Who is he?

ANSWERS

1.

1982, when they took Jim McMahon #5

2.

Chuck Howley and
Don Meredith, respectively

3.

Rashaan Salaam

4.

Jack Concannon

5.

Mark Bortz

Seasonal Stumper Answer:

Dick Gordon
(Dick Clark was the host.)

TWEENERS

1. Thomas Jones led the Bears in rushing from 2004-06. Matt Forte has done it since 2008. Who was their leader in 2007?

2. He was the head coach of the Bears between Mike Ditka and Dick Jauron.

3. While he played 13 years in Chicago, his Bears career was sandwiched between one-year stints with the Patriots in 1980 and Packers in 1994. Who is he?

4. The Bears won at least 10 games every season from 1984-1991...except one. What was their record in 1989?

5. Who was the team president of the Bears between George Halas, Jr. and Ted Phillips?

Before Matt Forte, the Bears went 20 years without having a running back represented in the Pro Bowl. Who made it in 1991?

ANSWERS

1.

Cedric Benson

2.

Dave Wannstedt

3.

Steve McMichael

4.

6-10

5.

Michael McCaskey, from 1983-99

Neal Anderson

STADIA-MANIA

1. In 1932, the NFL held its first-ever playoff game to break a tie in the standings between the Bears and Portsmouth Spartans. What was odd about the host facility, Chicago Stadium?

2. In 1986, the NFL came to England as the Bears and Cowboys played an exhibition contest with over 85,000 looking on at what venue?

3. Chicago won all but one of their NFL championships during their tenure at what venue?

4. While Soldier Field was being renovated, where did the Bears play their 2002 home games?

5. Fact or Fib? Soldier Field is the smallest football stadium in the NFL.

What Bear appeared on the cover of
Sports Illustrated in 1970 with the caption
"The Most Feared Man in the Game"?

ANSWERS

1.
Because the arena was smaller, special rules were adopted, including an 80-yard long field. The Bears ended up winning, 9-0.

2.
Wembley Stadium
(The Bears won, 17-6.)

3.
Wrigley Field

4.
Memorial Stadium, on the University of Illinois campus in Champagne

5.
Fib – It was until the 2013 season, when the Raiders reduced their Oakland Coliseum seating capacity by 10,000 to avoid local TV blackouts.

Dick Butkus

"O" My

These players first or last names begin with the letter O.

1. He led the AFC in sacks the year before he came to Chicago in 2004, but only hit double-digits once in six seasons as a Bear.

2. This 2007 first round pick of Chicago was traded to the Panthers in '11.

3. He had 10.5 sacks during the Bears 1985 Super Bowl season.

4. He holds the Bears record for the most wins as a rookie starting quarterback.

5. This seven-time Pro Bowl offensive tackle with another team wound up his career with the Bears in 2009.

Mike Brown made NFL history in 2001 with back-to-back overtime interception returns for scores to beat what two teams in consecutive weeks?

ANSWERS

Adewale Ogunleye

Greg Olsen

Otis Wilson

Kyle Orton, who went 10-5 in 2005

Orlando Pace

49ers and Browns

HANGIN' 'EM UP

Match up the following old-time Bears with the numbers that have been retired in their honor.

1. Bulldog Turner   a. 7

2. George Halas   b. 3

3. George McAfee   c. 56

4. Bronko Nagurski   d. 66

5. Bill Hewitt   e. 5

❄ SEASONAL STUMPER ❄

In 1989, the Bears missed the playoffs for the first time in six seasons. On Christmas Eve, who played the role of Grinch and ended Chicago's season with a 26-0 drubbing for their sixth-straight loss?

ANSWERS

1.

d

2.

a

3.

e

4.

b

5.

c

Seasonal Stumper Answer:

San Francisco 49ers

CHEESEHEAD CLASHES

1. In the Super Bowl era, had the Bears and Packers ever played before in the postseason prior to their 2010 NFC Championship meeting?

2. A 1980 game saw the largest margin of victory in the history of the two teams' rivalry. Who won in a 61-7 rout?

3. In a 1986 Packers-Bears game, what Green Bay nose tackle body-slammed Jim McMahon on a late hit and received the first multi-game suspension for an on-field incident in the NFL?

4. Because of its controversial ending, a 1989 contest between the Bears and Packers became known as the "Instant Replay" game. What happened?

5. In the 2006 opener, the Bears did something to Brett Favre that he hadn't experienced before in his 16-year career. What was it?

In 2007, what former Bears receiver married female boxing champ Laila Ali?

ANSWERS

1. No – They did, however, meet way back in the 1941 postseason. Chicago won, 33-14.

2. Bears

3. Charles Martin

4. With Chicago up and time running out, the Pack scored on a TD pass that was overturned because their QB was past the line of scrimmage- but the call went up to a replay official who then awarded the Packers the score, and a 14-13 win.

5. They shut him out, 26-0.

Curtis Conway

THE THREE BEARS

1.

The numbers 40, 41 and 42 have been retired for what three Bears?

2.

Who were the three QBs on the Super Bowl XX championship roster?

3. Three Bears accounted for all of Chicago's scoring in their 29-17 loss to the Colts in Super Bowl XLI. Can you name them?

4. Three great Bears, Dick Butkus, Red Grange and George Halas all went to one great school. What was it?

5. What three Bears have thrown over 25 touchdown passes in a single season?

What defensive coordinator was the architect of the 46 Defense, which played a huge role in bringing the Bears the 1985 NFL title?

ANSWERS

1.

Gale Sayers, Brian Piccolo and
Sid Luckman, respectively

2.

Jim McMahon,
Steve Fuller and Mike Tomczak

3. Devin Hester (92-yard TD kickoff return),
Muhsin Muhammad (4-yard TD pass
from Rex Grossman) and Robbie Gould
(44-yard FG and two extra points)

4.

University of Illinois

5.

Erik Kramer, Sid Luckman and Jay Cutler

Buddy Ryan

SWEETNESS

1. As a college sophomore in 1972, Walter Payton scored seven touchdowns as he led what school to a 72-0 win over Lane?

2. Fact or Fib? In his very first NFL game, Walter Payton surpassed 200 yards rushing.

3. When Payton set the new all-time rushing mark in 1984, whose record did he break?

4. Was Payton ever named the NFL's MVP?

5. Which of the following rushing records does Walter Payton still hold to this day?
   a. Most yards in a game   b. Most career TDs
   c. Most 100-yard games   d. None of the above

Who racked up over 2,200 yards receiving in the only two seasons he spent in Chicago from 1994-95?

ANSWERS

1.

Jackson State

2.

Fib – He carried the ball eight times for a total of zero yards.

3.

Jim Brown

4.

Yes – He received the honor in 1977.

5.

d (He held all of those marks at the time of his retirement, but has since been surpassed.)

Jeff Graham

GAMERS

1. What long snapper, whose career began in 1998, has played more games in a Bears uniform than anyone else?

2. How many games did Walter Payton miss in his 13-year NFL career?

3. What Hall of Famer, who ended his career in Chicago, is the NFL's all-time leader in consecutive starts by a defensive tackle?

4. Who started all but one game at center for the Bears from 2001-2010 before moving on to New Orleans the following year?

5. With a career spanning from 1949-75, what 1950s Bear played in the NFL in four different decades?

❄ SEASONAL STUMPER ❄

He might have been a Bear, but his last name rhymes with one of Santa's reindeer. In 2005, he returned a missed field goal 108 yards for a touchdown, which at the time set a new NFL record. Who is he?

ANSWERS

1.

Patrick Mannelly

2.

1

3.

Alan Page

4.

Olin Kreutz

5.

George Blanda

Seasonal Stumper Answer:

Nathan Vasher
(Dasher is the reindeer.)

WHO SAID IT?

1. What was this quarterback's best memory from his days at Brigham Young? "Leaving."

2. The first Bears rookie to lead the team in tackles explained that, "Most football teams are temperamental. That's 90% temper and 10% mental."

3. This Bears Super Bowl XX starting center once said, "The thing I like about football is that you don't have to take a shower to go to work."

4. During Super Bowl week, "Danimal" said of his QB, "If they tell Jim McMahon we have a ten o'clock curfew, he'll probably think that means 10 A.M. the next day."

5. The man who Dick Butkus nicknamed "Captain Who" before a Colts/Bears game described Butkus as an animal- "He doesn't shower after a game. He licks himself clean."

After his death in 1983, what award did the NFL rename the George Halas Trophy?

ANSWERS

1.

Jim McMahon

2.

Doug Plank

3.

Jay Hilgenberg

4.

Dan Hampton

5. Alex Hawkins (When the team captains were introduced, Butkus responded to the official's reference to "Captain Hawkins" by blurting out , "Captain Who?".)

The NFC Championship Trophy

PAPA BEAR

1. Before George Halas took control of Chicago's franchise in the early 1920s, he had a brief stint as an outfielder with what baseball team in 1919?

2. Halas is a Hall of Fame coach, but was no slouch as a player. He made the NFL's 1920s All-Decade Team at what position?

3. Halas' perfection of the T-formation attack created a revolutionary style of play that helped the Bears demolish what opponent, 73-0, in the 1940 NFL Championship Game?

4. Fact or Fib? Halas coached the Bears for every single season from 1920-67.

5. What football landmark is located on George Halas Drive?

What team sacked Jay Cuter nine times in the first half in an embarrassing 2010 Chicago defeat?

ANSWERS

1.

New York Yankees

2.

He was a two-way end (wide receiver on offense, defensive end on defense).

3.

Washington Redskins

4.

Fib – He stepped away a few different times to serve in the military.

5.

The Pro Football Hall of Fame, in Canton, Ohio

New York Giants

A Simple Yes or No Will Do

1.
Have the Bears ever had the #1 overall pick in the NFL Draft?

2.
Do the Bears have more Hall of Famers than any NFL franchise?

3.
Have the Bears ever had a cheerleading squad?

4.
Up until 2013 when Brian Urlacher retired, had he and Lance Briggs played every NFL season together in Chicago?

5.
Did Lovie Smith ever have a losing season in Chicago before getting fired after the 2012 season?

In their 1985 Super Bowl season, the Bears shut out what two opponents in back-to-back regular season games?

ANSWERS

1.

Yes, twice – Way back in 1941 and '47.

2.

Yes

3.

Yes – The Chicago Honey Bears were born in the late 1970s and performed at games through Super Bowl XX.

4.

No – Urlacher was drafted in 2000, three years before Briggs.

5.

Yes – He had three.

Dallas Cowboys and Atlanta Falcons

BROTHERLY LOVE

1. In 2006, two siblings made NFL history by each rushing for 1,000 yards. Name the Bear and his brother.

2. This Bear ended his career in 1993 in New Orleans where he teamed with his brother, Joel, a ten-year Saint and fellow Pro Bowl lineman. Who is he?

3. What co-owner of the Bears in the 1920s played alongside his brother, Joey, who quarterbacked Chicago for most of that decade?

4. Walter Payton's brother Eddie led the NFL in kick return yardage in 1980 and the following year had a 99-yard return TD with what team?

5. He had over 100 receptions with the Bears and his brother Byron, who ran for nearly 4,000 yards in the NFL, had a cup of coffee in Chicago in 1998. Name the pair.

❄ SEASONAL STUMPER ❄

"Bah! Humbug!" He left the Bears in 2003 after back-to-back double-digit sack seasons to join the Patriots. His name brings to mind the President who banned Christmas trees from the White House in the early 1900s.

ANSWERS

1.
Thomas Jones and brother
Julius Jones, with the Cowboys

2.
Jay Hilgenberg

3.
Dutch Sternaman

4.
Minnesota Vikings

5.
Ron Morris and Byron "Bam" Morris

Seasonal Stumper Answer:

Rosevelt Colvin

(Teddy Roosevelt banned the trees because
of his strong environmental feelings.)

ON ALL FOURS

1. What Hall of Famer was the first Bears player to catch four touchdown passes in one game?

2. While he only had five on the season, in 1983, what Bear recorded four sacks in the season opener?

3. What four men have been named the AP NFL Coach of the Year with Chicago?

4. What member of the 1940s NFL All-Decade Team had four interceptions in the five NFL Championship games he played in?

5. More recently, who became the first Chicago rookie QB ever to have a 300-yard, four-touchdown game?

Since Devin Hester has been in the NFL, only one other Bear has returned a punt for a touchdown. Who?

ANSWERS

1.

Mike Ditka, in 1963

2.

Jim Osborne

3.

George Halas, Mike Ditka,
Dick Jauron and Lovie Smith

4.

Bulldog Turner

5.

Cade McNown, in 1999

Earl Bennett

WELL RECEIVED

1.
Only one player has surpassed 5,000 yards receiving as a Bear. Who?

2.
What receiver, who began his career in Chicago in 1998, caught three touchdowns in a game for three different NFL teams?

3.
In his 2009 Pro Bowl rookie season, his first NFL catch went for 68 yards. Who is he?

4.
Fact or Fib? Walter Payton is the Bears all-time leader in receptions.

5.
What two Bears receivers who were teammates in 1999 each threw two touchdown passes in their Chicago careers?

What famous Bears nickname was first used by the University of Chicago football team in the early 1900s?

ANSWERS

1.

Johnny Morris (5,059)

2.

Marcus Robinson

3.

Johnny Knox

4.

Fact

5.

Curtis Conway and Marty Booker

Monsters of the Midway

BEARS 'BACKERS

1. Often credited as the first middle linebacker in the history of football, who shared Chicago's kicking duties with fellow Hall of Famer George Blanda in 1954?

2. Mike Singletary got his first coaching job in the NFL in 2003 as a linebackers coach with what team?

3. In 1989, what Michigan State player won the Dick Butkus Award as college's top linebacker before he joined the Bears for one year in 1993?

4. What Bear had an "unofficial" 18 sacks in 1968 and retired holding the team record for interceptions by a linebacker?

5. Which Bear is a member of the NFL's 20/20 Club (20 sacks and 20 interceptions): Brian Urlacher or Lance Briggs?

Lovie Smith made his first trip to the Super Bowl in 2001 as the defensive coordinator for what team?

ANSWERS

1.
   Bill George

2.
   Baltimore Ravens

3.
   Percy Snow

4.
   Doug Buffone

5.
   Brian Urlacher

St. Louis Rams

School Days

1. While he would later be surpassed, what Bears running back finished his career at Florida in 1985 as the school's all-time leading rusher?

2. What North Alabama standout who also starred with the Bears has an award named after him that is comparable to the Heisman Trophy at the Division II level?

3. Walter Payton's son Jarrett was college teammates with Kellen Winslow, Jr., another son of a Hall of Famer, at what school?

4. What 1980s Bear played alongside future Redskins Mark May and Russ Grimm and blocked for Dan Marino at Pittsburgh?

5. At what school did Brian Urlacher score several touchdowns as both a kick returner and receiver?

❄ Seasonal Stumper ❄

This defensive back was born on Christmas Eve, 1983, just a month after the holiday classic *A Christmas Story* first hit theatres. He became a hit in Chicago in 2012 after he had a hand in the first three interceptions of Andrew Luck's career. Name him.

ANSWERS

1.

Neal Anderson

2.

Harlon Hill (The Harlon Hill Trophy)

3.

University of Miami

4.

Jimbo Covert

5.

University of New Mexico

Seasonal Stumper Answer:

Tim Jennings (He picked Luck off twice and tipped another pass that led to the third interception.)

MANY HAPPY RETURNS

1. What Bear led the NFL in interceptions returned for touchdowns two seasons in a row with two in 2011 and three in '12?

2. In 1998, his first season in Chicago, who led the NFL in kick return yardage and ran back two for scores?

3. Before Devin Hester, who was the only Bear to return two punts for touchdowns in one season?

4. In 2010, Hester broke the career record for the most combined kick/punt return TDs in NFL history. What was the historic number?

5. In the 1985 Playoffs vs. the Giants, what Bear recorded the shortest punt return TD in NFL history after the wind caused New York punter Sean Landeta to whiff at the ball?

Why didn't the 1985 Super Bowl champion Bears make a trip to the White House?

ANSWERS

1.

Charles Tillman

2.

Glyn Milburn

3.

Dennis McKinnon, in 1987

4.

14

5.

Shaun Gayle, at five yards

Two days after their victory, the space shuttle
Challenger disaster occurred, and the trip was cancelled.

MULTI-SPORT STUDS

1. Long before his coaching days with the Bears, he was drafted by the both the Lions and MLB's St. Louis Cardinals in 1973. Name him.

2. What Bears receiver made the 1980 Olympic track team (the year the U.S. boycotted) and also had a stint as a Winter Olympic bobsledder?

3. Julius Peppers played both football and basketball in college, appearing in the 2000 Final Four with what squad?

4. Bronko Nagurski was a multiple world champion in this sport, and was posthumously inducted into its Hall of Fame in 2011.

5. Four years before he was a first round pick of the Bears, he was a 12th round selection of the L.A. Dodgers in 2001 and played in their summer league that year.

The 1934 NFL Championship Game, in which the Bears lost to the Giants, has become known in NFL lore by what nickname?

ANSWERS

1.

Dick Jauron

2.

Willie Gault

3.

North Carolina Tarheels

4.

Wrestling

5.

Cedric Benson

The Sneakers Game - The Giants scored 27 unanswered points in the second half after switching to basketball sneakers for better footing on the frozen Polo Grounds surface, winning 30-13.

THE LONGEST YARD

1. His first NFL touchdown came on a 90-yard fumble recovery in 2001. He would get another on an 85-yard interception return in 2007. Who is he?

2. Two Bears accounted for the longest TD pass in the NFL for four consecutive years- One in 1958 (as a Ram) and '61 and the other in 1959 and '60. Can you name either?

3. Since the 1950s, who's the only Bears back to have a run go for at least 80 yards?

4. Against what team did Devin Hester run back a missed field goal 108 yards for a touchdown in 2006?

5. In 1962, what Bears All-Pro had a league-leading 212 interception return yards, with almost half of that coming on a 101-yard runback for a score?

The son of what late Chicago Bear, who died in a car accident at age 29, became the first black U.S. Olympic gymnast?

ANSWERS

1.

Brian Urlacher

2.

Billy Wade and Ed Brown, respectively

3.

Neal Anderson, in 1988

4.

New York Giants

5.

Richie Petitbon

Willie Galimore (son Ron Galimore)

QUICK KICKS

1.
   What Bears kicker led the
   NFL in scoring in 1985?

2.
   Along with the answer to #1, what
   other two players have made at least
   ten 50-yard field goals as Bears?

3.
   In addition to being the team's punter,
   what Bear wore the #86 and was listed
   as a tight end for much of his Chicago
   career that lasted from 1972-83?

4.
   While he only played two NFL seasons,
   who pulled off the longest punt in Bears
   history with an 87-yard boom in 1984?

5.
   While in college, Mike Ditka was
   not just a star tight end for the
   University of Pittsburgh. Was he the
   team's kicker, punter or both?

❄ SEASONAL STUMPER ❄

Chicago suffered a Christmas hangover on
December 26, 1977 with their worst playoff loss in the
Super Bowl era. Who took them down in a 37-7 rout?

ANSWERS

1.

Kevin Butler

2.

Robbie Gould and Paul Edinger

3.

Bob Parsons

4.

Dave Finzer

5.

Punter

Seasonal Stumper Answer:

Dallas Cowboys

PLAYOFFS?!?

1. Who did the Bears defeat in their 1998 Divisional Playoff contest that became known as the Fog Bowl because of the limited visibility at Soldier Field?

2. What two teams have the Bears defeated multiple times each at Soldier Field in the postseason?

3. Walter Payton's career came to an end with a second consecutive postseason loss to what team in the 1987 Divisional Playoffs?

4. The Bears have been shut out once in the postseason. What team took them down in the 1984 NFC Championship?

5. From 1992-2006, the Bears won just one playoff game. Who was it against?

Who handed the Bears their worst-ever home defeat by beating them 34-0 in 1974 at Soldier Field?

ANSWERS

1.

Philadelphia Eagles, 20-12

2.

New Orleans Saints and
Seattle Seahawks

3.

Washington Redskins

4.

San Francisco 49ers, 23-0

5.

Minnesota Vikings, 35-18,
in the 1994 Playoffs

49ers

BIRTHDAY BOYS

1. This Bears Hall of Famer who made two All-Decade Teams has the same birthday, December 9, as entertainer Donny Osmond, who was born 15 years later in 1957.

2. While he's 36 years older, *Sunday Night Football's* Al Michaels shares his November 12 birthday with this Bear, born in 1980, whose fifth career TD came on *Monday Night Football* in 2012.

3. Tiger Woods and LeBron James share a birthday with this kicker, born December 30, 1981, who holds the Bears mark for consecutive field goals made, with 26.

4. Months after winning the Super Bowl in his lone All-Pro season, this Bear turned 27 on the same day that speedster Usain Bolt was celebrating his first day, August 21, 1986.

5. Both born on March 23, this Bears "Beast" is 11 years younger than future NBA Hall of Famer Jason Kidd, who was born in 1973.

In 1998, what Bears rookie ran for 163 yards in his first NFL start?

ANSWERS

1.

Dick Butkus

2.

Lance Briggs

3.

Robbie Gould

4.

Jim McMahon

5.

Brandon Marshall

James Allen

SECOND GUESSING

1. Only two players in Bears history are credited with over 60 sacks. Richard Dent, with 124.5, is first. With 92.5, who ranks second?

2. For just the second time in NFL history, a game ended in overtime on a safety when the Bears defeated what squad in 2004?

3. What quarterback became the second Bear ever to rush for four touchdowns in a single game in 1973?

4. The Bears nine NFL championships ranks second in league history behind what team?

5. Who dropped to second for most receiving yards in a season as a Bear when Brandon Marshall topped him in 2012?

In 1973, who became the first Bear to be named the Defensive Rookie of the Year?

ANSWERS

1.
Steve McMichael

2.
Tennessee Titans, 19-17

3.
Bobby Douglass

4.
Green Bay Packers

5.
Marcus Robinson

Wally Chambers

TALE OF THE TAPE

1.
Who's taller,
Julius Peppers or Michael Jordan?

2.
"I've been big ever since I was
little." What Bear with the
largest-ever Super Bowl ring size said it?

3.
What former Bears lineman, who
once tipped the scales at over 400
pounds, ranked as the NFL's
heaviest player in the early 2000s?

4.
In a humorous moment during a 2012
game, Jay Cutler bent down to tie the size
22 shoe of what Bears offensive tackle?

5.
Dick Butkus, Mike Singletary and
Brian Urlacher- who was the
heaviest of these great linebackers?

❄ SEASONAL STUMPER ❄

The year before *Santa Claus Is Coming to Town*
was first recorded in 1934, the Bears played for the
last time in a 12-year Thanksgiving Day tradition
against the team who now joins them as the only
remaining franchises from the NFL's inception.

ANSWERS

1.

Peppers, at 6'7", is an inch taller.

2.

William "Refrigerator" Perry

3.

Aaron Gibson

4.

J'Marcus Webb

5.

Urlacher, at 258 pounds (Butkus weighed 245 and Singletary, 230)

Seasonal Stumper Answer:

Chicago (now Arizona) Cardinals

THE NAME GAME

Each Bears figure below shares his full name
with another notable. Name them.

1. A 1981 Bears first round pick, he
   spent his entire 13-year career in
   Chicago. He shares his name with the
   second pick of the 1997 NBA Draft.

2. This Bears coach and Bud Grant are the only
   two men to have both played and coached
   in the NFL and CFL. His namesake wasn't
   known for sports...He was a little "spacey."

3. This 1999 Walter Payton Award
   winner and 2000s Bear will be
   remembered because his name mirrors
   that of a more accomplished NFL back.

4. While he was drafted by the Bears in 1965,
   he opted for the AFL, where he twice led the
   league in rushing. He's not to be confused with a
   sportscaster who has called multiple Super Bowls.

5. This former Bear became a first-time Pro Bowler
   at cornerback after he joined the 49ers in 2006.
   Division rival Larry Fitzgerald was coached by
   his namesake at the University of Pittsburgh.

In 1980, who became the first Bears
quarterback to post a perfect 158.3 rating in a game?

ANSWERS

1.

Keith Van Horne
(Keith Van Horn is the basketball player.)

2.

Neill Armstrong
(Neil Armstrong was the first
person to walk on the moon.)

3.

Adrian Peterson

4.

Jim Nance
(Jim Nantz is the sportscaster.)

5.

Walt Harris

Vince Evans

SUPER BOWL XLI

1. The Bears were defeated by the Colts, 29-17, in Super Bowl XLI on February 4, 2007. Where was the game played?

2. The contest was the first to feature two African-American head coaches. Name them.

3. While he didn't score a touchdown in the game, what Bear had the most receiving yards for his team?

4. Who was the game's MVP?

5. What weather-related phenomenon was unique about this Super Bowl?

Who was known as the Minister of Defense before Reggie White?

ANSWERS

1.

Sun Life Stadium
(then Dolphin Stadium), in Miami

2.

Lovie Smith and Tony Dungy

3.

Desmond Clark, with 64

4.

Peyton Manning

5.

It was the first time that rain
fell throughout the game.

Mike Singletary

THE AWARD GOES TO...

1. What Bear won the Jim Thorpe Award as the nation's top defensive back in 1989 and the NFL's Defensive Rookie of the Year in 1990?

2. The year after Walter Payton's name was added to the NFL Man of the Year Award, what Chicago defensive lineman was the recipient in 2000?

3. What Bear was the NFL's Defensive Player of the Year twice during the 1980s?

4. Who was the last Bear to be named Rookie of the Year?

5. Before coming to the Bears in 2013, Marc Trestman was the 2009 CFL Coach of the Year with what franchise?

In their 39-14 win over the Saints in the 2006 NFC Championship Game, who was the only Bears wide receiver to reach the end zone?

ANSWERS

1.

Mark Carrier

2.

Jim Flanigan

3.

Mike Singletary

4.

Anthony Thomas, in 2001

5.

Montreal Alouettes

Bernard Berrian

ALPHABET SOUP

1. In 1984, the Bears added the initials GSH to their jerseys in honor of George Halas. What did the "S" stand for?

2. What two Bears, who each have a "z" in their last name, were both Pro Bowlers in 2003?

3. What 10-year Bear, who went by his initials, technically caught the first TD pass ever thrown by Johnny Unitas when he intercepted Unitas for a "pick-six"?

4. What does the "O" in long-time Bears tackle James O. Williams stand for?

5. Just two letters should provide you with the losing quarterback in the 1963 NFL Championship Game, which the Bears won, 14-10.

❄ SEASONAL STUMPER ❄

When the Bears played the Packers on New Years Eve 2006 and Christmas 2011 (both losses), two unlikely quarterbacks threw Chicago's only TD passes. They share their first names with the men who recorded *Angels We Have Heard on High* on the quintuple platinum 2007 Christmas Album *Noel*.

ANSWERS

1.

Stanley, his middle name

2.

Jerry Azumah and Olin Kreutz

3.

J.C. Caroline

4.

Otis

5.

Y.A. Tittle, of the Giants

Seasonal Stumper Answer:

Brian Griese and Josh McCown
(Brian McKnight and Josh Groban sang
the duet on Groban's album.)

LAST CALL

Match each well-known Bear with
the last NFL team he played for.

1. Mike Ditka   a. San Diego Chargers

2. Thomas Jones   b. Philadelphia Eagles

3. Jim Harbaugh   c. Kansas City Chiefs

4. William Perry   d. Detroit Lions

5. Alonzo Spellman   e. Dallas Cowboys

What #46 was the inspiration for the
naming of the Bears vaunted 46 Defense?

ANSWERS

1.

e

2.

c

3.

a

4.

b

5.

d

Doug Plank